Flowers to Spot

Illustrated by Stephanie Fizer Coleman
Designed by Jenny Brown

Words by Sam Smith and
Kirsteen Robson

You can use the stickers to fill in the chart
at the back of the book, so you can keep
track of the flowers that you have seen.

The months in the description for each plant
show the time of year when it flowers.

Towns and roadsides

Daisy

Small plant with rounded leaves a
base. Common on lawns. Flowers
close at night and in rain to keep
pollen dry. January-October.

Rosebay willow-herb

Tall plant with spikes of pink
flowers and long, narrow leaves.
Common on railway banks and
disused land. July-September.

Dandelion clock

Dandelion

Common weed with a base of toothed
leaves. Look for the downy white
'clock' of seeds. March-June.

Houseleek

A rosette plant with fleshy leaves
and dull-red, spiky petals. Does
not flower every year. Look on
old walls and roofs. June-July.

Usually you will only see the
houseleek's rosette without a stalk.

Ivy-leaved toadflax

Slender stalks trail on old walls.
Look for yellow parts on its
mauve flowers. May-September.

Stinging nettle

Its toothed leaves are covered
with stinging hairs. Dangling
green-brown flowers. Common
in many places. June-August.

3

Hedgerows

Rose hip

Dog rose
Creeping plant with thorny stems and sweet-smelling flowers. Look for its red fruits, called rose hips, in autumn. Hedges and woods. June-July.

Cow parsley
Look for the ribbed stem, feathery leaves and white flower clusters. Hedgebanks and ditches. May-June.

Herb Robert
A spreading plant with a strong smell. Leaves are red in autumn. Hedgebanks and woods. May-September.

Blackberry

A dense, woody plant that climbs up hedges. Sharp prickles on stems and under leaves. Edible berries are ripe in autumn. June-September.

White dead-nettle

White or greenish-white flowers. Its hairy leaves do not sting. Hedges and bare ground. March-November.

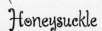

Honeysuckle

Sweet-smelling climbing plant with yellowish-cream flowers tinged with orange, red or lilac. Hedges and woods. May-August.

Fields and meadows

Creeping buttercup

Shiny yellow flowers. Long, trailing
stems and hairy leaves. Grows close to
ground in grassy places. May-August.

Meadow thistle

Dark red or purple flowers and
prickly leaves. Prefers damp,
boggy areas. June-August.

Cowslip

Easily recognized by the single
clusters of drooping flowers.
Found in meadows. April-May.

Oxeye daisy

Tall, upright plant with large white and yellow flowers and toothed leaves. Grassy places and roadsides. June-August.

Fritillary or Snake's head

Its drooping bell-shaped flowers are checkered with light and dark purple. Woods and damp meadows. May.

Flowers may also be white with pink or green veins.

Red clover

Reddish-purple or pale pink flowers. Groups of three oval leaves. Common in grassy places. May-October.

Woods

Primrose

Spring flower with a hairy stem
and a base of wrinkled leaves.
Grows in patches in woods,
hedges and fields. December-May.

Foxglove

Upright plant with a tall spike of
trumpet-shaped flowers, drooping on
one side of the stem. Very poisonous.
Open woods. June-September.

Wood anemone

Forms carpets in woods.
Look for pink streaks on
the outside of the petals.
March-June.

Red campion
Upright woodland plant with a hairy, sticky stem and opposite pairs of pointed, oval leaves. May-June.

Wood woundwort
Spikes of dark red flowers. Its toothed leaves give off a strong, unpleasant smell. Woods, hedgerows and roadsides. June-August.

Spur

Common dog violet
Creeping woodland plant with heart-shaped leaves and short spurs on the flowers. April-June.

9

Woods

Lesser celandine

Small, creeping plant with glossy, heart-shaped leaves and shiny yellow flowers. Look in damp, shady woods and on roadsides. March-May.

Yellow archangel

Look for the red-brown markings on the yellow petals. Toothed leaves grow opposite each other in pairs. May-June.

Snowdrop

Nodding white flowers smell like honey. Dark green leaves are long and flat. January-March.

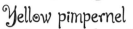

Yellow pimpernel

Slender creeping plant with
trailing stems, and oval or
heart-shaped leaves. Woods
and hedges. May-September.

Bluebell

Narrow, shiny leaves and clusters
of nodding purplish-blue flowers.
Forms thick carpets in woods.
April-May.

Bluebell flower.

Bugle

Creeping plant with upright flower
spikes. Purplish stem is hairy. Forms
carpets in damp woods. May-June.

Rivers, ponds and streams

White water-lily
Forms blankets of floating leaves
on still or slow-moving water.
White flowers are deeply
cup-shaped. June-September.

Yellow water-lily
Forms leafy mats on slow-moving
water. Yellow, cup-shaped flowers
held out of the water on long,
firm stems. June-September.

Flowers can be pink,
purple or white.

Policeman's helmet
Flowers look like open mouths. Rip
seed pods burst when touched. Nea
rivers and streams. July-October.

Frogbit
Rises to the water's surface in spring.
Shiny round leaves grow in tufts.
Canals and ponds. July-August.

Purple loosestrife
Hairy stem and leaves. Grows in
clumps by streams and rivers,
and on marshes. June-September.

Water crowfoot
Anchors its roots in mud at the
bottom of ponds and streams.
Flowers cover the water's
surface. May-June.

13

Coast and seashore

Golden samphire

Grows on sea cliffs and salt marshes.
Large yellow flower heads and
narrow, fleshy leaves. July-August.

Yellow horned poppy

Single, flimsy yellow flowers,
and toothed leaves. Likes shingle
beaches. June-October.

Bloody cranesbill

Bushy plant with deeply-divided
leaves on hairy stems. Bright,
pinkish-purple flowers. Cliffs,
rocks and sand dunes. June-August.

Viper's bugloss

Blue flowers grow from pink buds.
Long, rough leaves on bristly stems.
Sand dunes and other dry, open,
stony places. June-September.

Thrift

Forms dense, low-growing mats of
grass-like leaves with small pink
flowers. Coastal rocks and salt
marshes. May-August.

Sea aster

Fleshy plant with spear-shaped leaves
and loose clusters of mauve or lilac
daisy-like flowers. Salt marshes and
sea cliffs. July-October.

Heaths and moors

Heath speedwell

Grows close to the ground in grassy places and woods. Flowers grow in upright spikes. Hairy oval leaves. May-August.

Goldenrod

Upright plant with stiff, leafy stems and flowers on thin spikes. Heaths, woods and rocky ground. July-September.

Gorse

Dark green spiny bush on heaths and commons. Bright yellow flowers smell of coconut and vanilla. March-June.

Heather or Ling
Grows in carpets on heaths and moors. Leafy spikes of tiny pink or white flowers shaped like bells. July-September.

Harebell
Slender, branching stem with nodding, violet-blue, bell-shaped flowers. Heaths and grassland. June-September.

Bird's-foot trefoil
Creeping plant. Yellow flowers have red streaks. Seed pods look like bird's claws. Grassland, sand dunes and rocks. May-September.

17

Marshes

Meadowsweet
Frothy clusters of sweet-smelling flowers. Grows in marshes, damp grassland, and by streams and ditches. May-September.

Marsh violet
Lilac flowers with dark purple veins and heart- or kidney-shaped leaves. April-July.

Marsh marigold
Shiny, yellow flowers and large heart-shaped leaves. Grows in clumps in wet places. March-June.

Great willow-herb

Forms large patches in riverbanks and ditches. Upright stems have pink, or sometimes white, flowers. June-September.

Devil's-bit scabious

Upright plant with bluish-purple, domed flower heads on long stalks. Wet, grassy places. June-October.

Ragged Robin

Upright plant with a forked stem has narrow, pointed leaves and flowers with pink, ragged petals. Marshes and damp places. May-June.

19

Bare ground

Larkspur

Slender plant with spikes of purple, pink or white flowers. A long spur sticks out behind each flower. Feathery leaves. June-July.

Larkspur flower

Cornflower

Blue flower heads above scaly, cup-shaped parts. Cornfields and bare ground. July-August.

St. John's wort

Clusters of deep yellow flowers and narrow, oval leaves. See-through dots on petals look like tiny holes. Bare ground and grassy places. June-September.

Wild pansy
Bright flowers can be any mixture of purple, yellow and white. Oval leaves. Bare ground and farmland. April-October.

Seed pod

Common poppy
Upright plant with stiff hairs on stem and soft red flowers. Round seed pods grow in late summer. Bare ground and farmland. June-August.

Greater bindweed
Climbs walls and hedges. Large, pink or white funnel-shaped flowers. July-September.

Spotting chart

Once you've spotted a flower from this book, find its sticker at the back, and stick it on this chart in the space below its name.

Bird's-foot trefoil	Blackberry	Bloody cranesbill	Bluebell	Bugle
Common dog violet	Common poppy	Cornflower	Cow parsley	Cowslip
Creeping buttercup	Daisy	Dandelion	Devil's-bit scabious	Dog rose
Foxglove	Fritillary	Frogbit	Goldenrod	Golden samph.
Gorse	Greater bindweed	Great willow-herb	Harebell	Heather

Heath speedwell	Herb Robert	Honeysuckle	Houseleek	Ivy-leaved toadflax
Larkspur	Lesser celandine	Marsh marigold	Marsh violet	Meadowsweet
Meadow thistle	Oxeye daisy	Policeman's helmet	Primrose	Purple loosestrife
Ragged Robin	Red campion	Red clover	Rosebay willow-herb	Sea aster
Snowdrop	Stinging nettle	St. John's wort	Thrift	Viper's bugloss
Water crowfoot	White dead-nettle	White water-lily	Wild pansy	Wood anemone
Wood woundwort	Yellow archangel	Yellow horned poppy	Yellow pimpernel	Yellow water-lily

Index

First published in 2019 by Usborne Publishing Ltd., Usborne House, 83-85 Saffron Hill, London EC1N 8RT, England.
www.usborne.com Copyright © 2019 Usborne Publishing Ltd. The name Usborne and the devices 🔱 ⊕ are Trade
Marks of Usborne Publishing Ltd.